I was a Brussel Sprout

Adrian Collman
Illustrated by James Venning Young

I was a Brussel Sprout

Written and published by Adrian John Collman
Illustrated by James Venning Young

A CIP catalogue record for this book is available from the British
Library

ISBN 978-0-9569197-0-0

First published by Adrian John Collman July 2011

For my beautiful little princess
Lily Ivy Stephanie Collman
'I will never give up'

Contents

I was a Brussel Sprout

Hello.

My name is Adrian.

I was a brussel sprout.

I'm a human now.

But it took special magic to turn me into a real person.

So here's my life story....

Being a Brussel

The Early Years

We were born in a muddy field and we were surrounded by mud. In fact there really wasn't much else around except for mud. I ate mud for

breakfast, lunch and dinner and if I was very good I was allowed to have a mud snack in the evening. On special occasions we were allowed to stay up late and we'd have a huge mud banquet. I used to love my lovely mud baths on a Sunday evening and I can still taste the delicious hot mug of mud my mum used to make me every night before bedtime.

One day however, I was taken from this mud heaven and my life changed forever. I was exposed to a mean world outside of my safe field. I noticed I was different to lots of the other vegetables and not all of them wanted to be my friend. They said I was revolting and that my family were responsible for some rather disgusting foul smells. Apparently some relations of mine always ruined Christmas dinner.

So here's where my story truly starts.

Kidnapped

One day I was fast asleep in the wonderful mud. Suddenly, I was woken by a huge roaring metal monster with silver claws and see-through eyes.

I was ripped from the ground and tossed in the air. I was terrified! Everywhere around me there were sprouts crying, sprouts screaming, sprouts fighting. Noise was coming from every direction.

"Ouch you hit me on my head!"

"You poked me in my eye!"

"Your tongue is up my nose!"

"Your elbow is in my ear!"

I couldn't even shout because someone had put their knee in my mouth.

And then we all landed in a large container. We were squashed together and none of us could move. We were starting to gasp for air. Some of the sprouts started to panic and clambered towards the top of the container but the slides were slippery and they just slipped back down. Then there was a large bang and we were plunged into darkness. Everyone stopped struggling and everything went silent.

A New Home

After a short journey in the darkness and a period of waiting around, I found myself in the most colourful place I had ever seen. There were giants walking everywhere, pushing some type of metal horse on wheels in front of them. They were grabbing things around them and throwing them gently into the mouths of these beasts. The strange things around me seemed desperate to be chosen.

"Pick me, I'm fresh!"

"I'm organic!"

"I'm from the value range!"

"Pick me and you can have one of my friends for free!"

Not long after I'd arrived on the shelf, a large pink thing with 5 pointy bits descended down and put

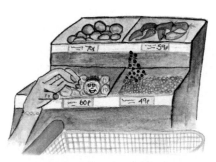

me, along with some other brussels, into a strange plastic thing. We didn't particularly like it in there because it was hard to breathe.

Luckily I have very good eyesight (better than a carrot's) and next to me I could see lots and lots of tiny green blobs. They looked just like me when I was a baby.

"Hello," I said. "Where are we?"

"Helloweareverypleasedtomeetyouwehaveneverseenanyonewholookslik eyoubeforeyoulooklikeabiggerversionofusonlyyouhavealovelyjacketonyou mustexcuseusifwegoonalittlebit becausewereallylovetotalk."

"Pardon?"

"Helloweareverypleasedtomeetyouwehaveneverseenanyonewholookslik eyoubeforeyoulooklikeabiggerversionofusonlyyouhavealovelyjacketonyou mustexcuseusifwegoonalittlebit becausewereallyloveto**talk**."

I didn't have a clue what they were talking about, they spoke way too fast...but it was something to do with going for a **walk** I thought.

"What's going to happen to me?" I asked.

"Wereallydonothavetheslightestideaeitherbecauseitisourfirsttimeheretoo youseebutsomeofusareveryexcitedandsomeofusareveryscaredandthereas onthatsomeofusarealittlebitfrightenedissomethingtodowithawordthatw ehavenoideawhatitmeansandthatwordis**teeth**."

Great, I thought, I have always wanted to see a **leaf**. And with that I drifted off into a deep sleep and dreamt of this wonderful stroll through the woods I was going to have tomorrow.

It truly was one of the nicest sleeps I had ever had, until...

"Hey, that tickles!" I was rudely woken by a giant who had just taken my green jacket off and was now tattooing an X on my bottom.

"Put me down!" I shouted.

And they did, straight into a freezing cold puddle surrounded by metal. I couldn't swim but luckily, being very round and fat, it turned out that I was very good at bobbing about in the water.

"Can't you make this hotter?" I pleaded.

"Be quiet you disgusting bogey, everybody hates you, everybody thinks you taste horrible," shouted a very rude, triangular, orange vegetable thing which had also come for a swim.

Next time you eat one of these orange vegetables, which apparently are called carrots, please don't feel sad about it. They really are the meanest vegetable in the world.

"Excuse me?"

"Oh be quiet you ugly ball of snot."

"My mum says I am very handsome."

"Then your mum is as stupid as you are. I bet she can't add up 1 and 1."

I started to defend my mum's honour when I noticed that it was getting hotter.

And hotter.

And then far too hot.

Before I knew it, I was scooped from this boiling puddle and was lying on a smooth, round, white thing. I touched my belly. Somehow it seemed ...softer!

"Are..you..okay?..
It..seems..to..me
..that..there..is..
the..possibility
..that..you..
might.. be..
rather..
frightened,..
or am..I..just..
simply..mistaken,
..which..can..often..be..the..case..with..
me?"

The question (which took forever to be spoken) came from an oval shaped, dirty brown vegetable.

"What is going to happen to me?" I asked.

"Well..that..is..a..very..interesting..
question..and..I..don't..really..know..
the..answer..to..it..just..yet..It's..my..
first..time..here..too..In..actual..fact..I..
would..only..be..guessing."

I stopped paying any interest to what he was saying after about a minute and started to daydream about mud. Ages later I realised that he was still talking and might actually have said something that could be useful.

Just as I was about to ask the kind vegetable to repeat his words of wisdom (which would have been a very painful experience....)

"Ouch!"

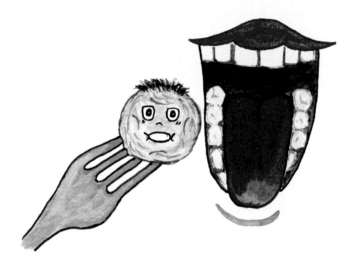

A huge metal thing with four sharp points stabbed me in my belly. I was lifted high into the air and was plunged into the darkness once more. Only this time there were white rocks crashing around me. A pink slimy thing was slurping all over me and I was covered in this gooey liquid.

Escape

Suddenly there was a huge, booming noise.
Yuk! Then there was a large gust of wind which
came from a black tunnel. This was followed by
a rush of orange triangles and a disgusting foul
smelling liquid that swept me along in a load of
chewed food and horrible, green, sticky water. I
flew through the air and landed in a large stinky
puddle on the floor. Another giant wiped me up
from the ground.

"Who has just been sick?" It asked.

Before I knew what was happening I was shaken
about by this giant and I had a very uncomfortable
landing in a white bowl which had a hole at the
bottom filled with water.

A large pool of this
sick stuff landed on top
of me. Yuk! Suddenly
a waterfall exploded
above me. The water
started to spin around.
I was being dragged
closer and closer to the
hole at the bottom.

Closer and closer.

Round and round.

Faster and faster.

Then...

"Whee!"

This was great fun. I was whizzing down a long slide, twisting, turning, spinning, upside down, back to front, over and over.

Until, Splash!

I was floating again.

But this time in a long winding stretch of water (a river). I was being carried onwards at quite a speed and during this journey I passed lots of strange objects:

Small metal containers (tins).

Rubber things that giants wear on their feet (wellies).

More of those metal horses that get pushed along (trolleys).

Some other metal horses that giants ride on (bicycles).

Large, black, round rubber things (tyres).

And for the record not one of them even said a word to me. How very rude!

The river became faster and faster and then wider and wider.

Suddenly there was a change.

All I could see everywhere was water.

Only this time the water was salty.

And rough.

I was moving further and further away from land.

But I was free and that was all because one of those giants didn't like me. Tasting disgusting clearly does have its advantages. So next time you're eating your Christmas dinner and your mum is making you eat your sprouts, remember, they want to be spat out, not eaten!

During my long journey in the salty water, which they call the sea, lots and lots of silver slimy things came to visit me. They were all shapes and sizes but none of them were friendly. Time and time again they tried to swallow me but on each occasion I was almost immediately coughed up. Clearly I really did taste horrible after all!

I saw some pretty disgusting creatures lurking below me as well. They had large claws and they shuffled along sideways. They were trying to pinch my bottom. But the worst thing of all for me was this horrible weedy stuff that was also floating in the sea and kept getting caught around me.

I bobbed along for days and days, occasionally being nibbled, occasionally being attacked by the weed of the sea and sometimes being pinched. As well as that, the water was starting to get really cold.

And little white chunks of ice started to float past me.

As the days went by, more and more of these ice blocks started to appear and some of them were really big.

There seemed to be more ice than water and I barely had room to bob up and down anymore.

Then everything became solid.

And I was no longer floating.

In the distance I could hear something wonderful.

Those sounds weren't my imagination. They were really coming from a fat jolly man dressed in red and white who was flying on a box pulled along by strange creatures with huge horns on their heads. The box didn't seem to be flying properly.

The Time I Nearly Ruined Christmas

The North Pole

"Ho, Ho, Ho Adrian. Do you want to help me with Christmas?" asked Father Christmas.

"Sure." I replied, even though I didn't have the slightest idea what Christmas was. But I wasn't busy and I fancied a change of scenery.

"I'm having trouble flying this sledge. I think there's something wrong with the brakes. Whilst I'm fixing it I need someone else to finish the toys off."

Now I'm sure you all know that Father Christmas is a great man. I've had the incredible privilege of working with him many times now and he really is amazing. But he's not perfect. Truthfully he's only jolly for one month a year. But that's because he has to spend from January to November doing his paperwork.

We go on holiday together now every summer and here are some things I have learnt about him.

1. He likes to play cards but he's a terrible loser and will storm off to bed in a strop if he loses, throwing all of his cards on the floor as he leaves.

2. He likes to play on the beach but insists on wearing sandals and socks as he hates the feel of sand sticking between his toes.

3. He loves raspberry slush puppies but always gets that sharp pain in his head when he drinks them.

4. He uses factor 50 sun cream because he once burned his nose very badly and everyone called him "Rudolph!".

5. He wears red and white Bermuda shorts and if you look closely you can see pictures of him on them.

6. He's a very fussy eater and he does not like anything with fish, tomatoes or apples in.

7. The sound of water being poured from a jug really annoys him, as does the sound of crisp packets being scrunched up.

In December, however, the magic takes hold of him. I was shocked to hear that there are some people in the world who don't believe in him. What a load of rubbish. How else do they think their presents arrive on Christmas Eve? Apparently mummies and daddies give out the presents! Well let me assure you that this only happens for the children who have stopped believing. I certainly still get presents from him every year.

While we're on the subject of Christmas here are some very important tips for you:-

1: Father Christmas really does know if you've been naughty or nice. One year my brother didn't get any presents at all, and now he knows exactly what will happen if he ever again takes money from a certain other family member's elephant-shaped piggy bank.

2: There's another reason why you really don't want to be put onto that naughty list. That's because it's quite hard to get your name removed from it once you are known as a troublemaker. You then have to be slightly better behaved than the nice children. This is something my brother has yet to manage. Until he is very good again, all he is going to keep on getting is a satsuma, a pair of socks and a knitted jumper.

3: Naturally I have never been on the naughty list because I have helped out the 'big fella'. But for goodness sake please don't call him the 'big fella'. That's a quick way to get on that naughty list. He's very sensitive about his weight. Remember that he only looks fat because he wears lots of thick, warm clothes when he has to deliver presents on cold winter's nights.

4: He does know if you're awake and he won't come down your chimney (or through your keyhole) until you are asleep. Naturally he will try to redeliver your presents at another time but there's a chance that he might not have time. Just ask Lily from Tottenham about December 2009. I guess that will teach her to stay up late and watch TV on Christmas Eve!

5: Please don't leave him too much brandy. He always drinks more of it than he should and then his sledge ends up flying all over the place. Milk really is fine, along with a nice biscuit and a carrot (ha ha, evil orange vegetable, my revenge is sweet!) for the reindeer of course.

Anyway, I'm forgetting to tell my story.

It came as a great shock to me
to learn that brussel sprouts
aren't that useful at carrying
out practical tasks. When
we landed, Father Christmas
announced that he needed
to make a few changes to my
appearance. I agreed as I'd
always considered myself to
have a rather crooked nose.
But before I could put in any
requests I noticed two things
sprouting (no pun intended)
from my bottom half and
two other things sprouting
(still no pun intended) out
of my side. They were called
arms and legs.

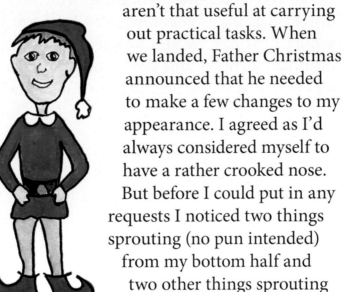

Everywhere around me I noticed thousands upon
thousands of green beings with arms and legs
just like mine. They all seemed incredibly happy
as they rushed about with arms full of colourful
packages. Behind them were wooden buildings
lit up by strings of bright lights, some of which
seemed to be twinkling. Muddy fields were great,
but nothing could compare to this place.

The Workshops

"I need you to help me paint these toys," said Father Christmas. "We only have a few more days before Christmas Eve and we need to add the finishing touches to this last lot of presents. These elves will be working next door to you and will show you what to do."

I turned to the tiny green elves next to me. There were lots of them but they were all much smaller than me. I looked closely at the toy. It was made of metal and had four round rubber things in each corner (they were smaller versions of the tyre things I saw floating in the river).

"What colour paint shall I use for each part?" I asked.

"Thatisaverygoodquestionitisveryimportantthatyougetalltherightcoloursi nalloftherightplacesotherwiseitcouldlookterribleyouputblackonthetyresof coursandonthesteeeringwheelandyoupaintthedoorsandthebonnetinreda ndyoudothehandlesinsilver."

"I get it, I get it!" I didn't get it! I couldn't understand a word they said, but how hard could it be?

I was going to just take my time and, despite my

lack of practical skills, I was determined to paint the most wonderful toy anyone had ever seen.

I was definitely going to produce something more stunning than anything Father Christmas had ever seen before. Every tiny part of this toy was treated with loving care. The tyres were painted in five different shades of black, the middle of these with seven shades of silver. The main body was painted in twenty-seven shades of red and even the tiniest mud splat (an area I was a specialist in) was painted very carefully. I was so proud of my toy. This truly was the greatest achievement of my life and I couldn't wait to show Father Christmas.

He always insists on inspecting every single toy before it is wrapped and placed in his sleigh. You'd be amazed to find out how many presents he sends back to be redone. I was certain, however, that he wouldn't find any fault with my work.

"Ho, Ho, Ho Adrian. Can I see what you have done today please?"

I handed him my masterpiece, unable to hide my self-satisfied glow. Let the compliments begin I thought...

"This is truly magnificent. The detail is incredible. I've never seen such care and attention," said a clearly impressed Father Christmas.

I felt a strange feeling that I had never experienced before. Something that made my green cheeks glow - pride!

"Can I see the other toys you've painted please?"

I felt an ice cold chill run right down my spine.

"Other toys?" I asked.

"Well obviously you've painted more than one toy today?" said Father Christmas, with a hint of concern in his voice.

The colour quickly drained again from my face. The rest of my workshop was empty. Another strange feeling washed over me. It was one that I have now grown very used to - shame!

As if timed to perfection, the door to the workshop next to me burst open, spilling out a host of tiny green elves on a huge wave of painted toys. Their huge workshop (bigger than the field I was born in) was full to the brim with millions and millions of cars. I really was a failure and I felt devastated.

Luckily, Father Christmas noticed that I was sad.

"Don't worry. We've time to fix this. The other elves will help out."

Father Christmas could've been furious with me and I could've been badly told off but instead he showed me kindness and that made me more determined than ever to never let him down again.

Feeling totally relaxed I went to bed for the night. I was going to wake up early the next day and prove to Father Christmas that I really was a great worker.

I was put to work the next morning next to a large elf with dirty brown hair. I knew my work involved some sharp, wooden sticks that people write with. Apparently I had to put a rubber on the ends of these. I was determined not only to get every little detail right but to produce so many of these so called pencils that my workshop would be full by the end of the day.

"So, how do I do this?" I asked my *painfully* slow speaking workmate.

"Well..that..is..a..very..good..question.. I..am..glad..that..you..have..asked.. it.. because..it..would..be..very..easy.. to.. make..a..mistake..Nobody..would.. like.. that..would..they?..So,..if..I..may.. explain..briefly..First..of..all..you..go.. to..this..table..and..get..a..pencil..and.. then..you..go..over..to..this..table..and.. get..a..rubber..and..then...

"I get it, I get it," I interrupted.

How hard could this be? It was easy. I just had to do everything really quickly and do more than my friend next to me, although I was pretty sure he wouldn't be breaking the speed limit today.

The rest of the day was just a blur. Stick, stick, stick, stick, stick. My newly formed arms were working at one million miles per hour. My workshop was filling up with pencils. Admittedly it was not full to the brim, but at the end of the day it was very clear that I had done loads more than my neighbour. I stood back and admired my success. Here comes Father Christmas. Let the praise begin.

"Ho, Ho, Ho, you really have been busy haven't you? May I see one of those please?"

I'm not sure that I had ever been more excited than I was at that very moment.

"Oh dear!" said a clearly distressed Father Christmas as he inspected the contents of my workspace.

I felt an awful feeling once again, the one that comes before shame – dread!

"Have you stuck rubbers on both ends of all of the pencils?"

I was not totally sure which part was the rubber and which part was the pencil, but I knew I had done something wrong.

"I am afraid that I cannot use any of these," said Father Christmas.

And then came that all too familiar feeling again -
shame.

"No-one will be able to write with these."

I wanted to run away there and then, but Father
Christmas was far too kind.

"Don't worry, we just about have time to fix this,
the other elves will help out again. Come outside
with me," he said. "I know a game that you're
really going to love."

And he was right, I had the most fun I'd ever had in my life.

When I went outside all of the elves were rolling up balls of snow. They each made about one hundred in ten seconds. The snow was freezing and when I tried to make a ball it took me forever just to make mine stick together.

Smack!

One of those balls hit me on the nose.

It had been thrown deliberately.

Smack! Smack!

One in my ear, one in my eye.

Smack! Smack! Smack! Smack! Smack!

I was being hit all over my body and I loved it.

The best advice I can ever give you is don't play this game if you don't like getting wet and cold. And certainly don't play this game against elves. You wouldn't believe how quickly they can make these snow balls, or how hard they can throw them, or how accurately they can throw them, or how many they can throw at one time!

But I learned about something new that evening - how to have fun. And that was all because Father Christmas showed faith in me and made me feel valued. He could have asked me to leave his workshop but instead I knew I was trusted and that made me keener than ever to do the most amazing job.

Once again I had a very happy night's sleep and when I woke up I noticed that everyone looked extra busy, in fact, even Father Christmas looked over-worked.

"Ho, ho, ho!" he bellowed. "It's Christmas Eve today. It's our last chance to finish and load the presents and we're still behind schedule on the teddy bear orders. I just need you to stick their smiles on."

He pointed me towards another workshop where an angry looking elf with orange hair was working.

I had no idea what a teddy was, or a bear, or a smile!

"Can you tell me what I have to do please?" I asked.

"No, work it out yourself!"

"Please help me. I don't want to make any mistakes today."

"I don't help stupid elves."

"Please!"

"Be quiet and leave me alone."

How rude! But this was surely going to be easy. So during the rest of the day I quickly stuck as many shapes as I possibly could onto as many cuddly toys as I could get my hands on.

When Father Christmas came to inspect these toys at the end of the day I noticed that his face quickly changed and his mouth now looked exactly like the mouths I had stuck on my cuddly toys. I got a terrible feeling that this was not a good thing.

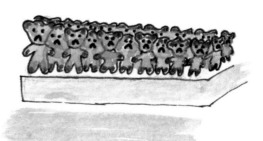

"Oh no, you have stuck the smiles on upside down. Every teddy bear looks really miserable. These are going to make all of the children really sad," said Father Christmas. "We don't have any time to repair these now, they'll just have to be delivered as they are."

Great!

I had done the impossible!

I had ruined Christmas!

"You're so stupid, you've spoiled everything. Why don't you get lost?" said my rude work colleague.

Running Away

I ran as fast as I could up towards the top of a large white hill. I felt like a failure. I felt like I had let down all of the brussel sprouts in the world. I'd been given the job that I had always wanted. I'd tried my best. But I'd failed. Was this my fault or was it the fault of some unhelpful elves?

I knew I could never go back to the workshop so before I got to the top of hill I decided to have one last look behind me. I noticed that all the elves also looked as miserable as my teddy bears and that there was something flowing from Father Christmas' eyes. Everyone was stood around the sledge, but they couldn't seem to make it move. It looked really stuck. I had a terrible feeling that I might not have helped things last night when I forgot to shut the door to the barn where the sleigh was kept.

Some of the elves were trying to push the sleigh but they all ended up in a heap on top of each other.

Some of the elves were trying to pull the sleigh but they just landed flat on their faces.

Some of the elves took running jumps at the sleigh

but bounced off it and fell over backwards.

There were elves lying everywhere. In some places just their boots were showing above the snow.

There was no way that anyone was going to be able to move that sledge. Father Christmas would not be able to deliver any of his presents. All of the children across the world would be miserable.

I turned around and ran.

And then I stumbled and fell.

And rolled over backwards.

And then started to tumble.

Head over heels.

Heels over head.

Arms over legs.

Nose over mouth.

Ears over bottom.

And the snow was starting to stick to me.

I was getting heavier and heavier.

Rounder and rounder.

Faster and faster.

There was nothing I could do but I was now rolling rapidly straight towards the sleigh.

All of the elves dived out of the way and I think I banged into Father Christmas, as the last thing I remember was a flying red and white thing.

Before:

Crash!

Silence.

Screams!

More screams!

Clapping!

Cheers!

More cheers!

"Adrian, you've saved Christmas!" said a delighted Father Christmas. "My sleigh was stuck in the ice and we couldn't get it out. But you've freed it and now I can deliver my presents after all."

"You're a hero!" shouted the elves.

And for one day I was, although some children might have been slightly disappointed with their depressed teddy bears that Christmas!

So next time you're rolling up a really big ball of snow, remember that it's actually a snow sprout and it's how people remember the day I saved Christmas.

The Time I Nearly Ruined Easter

Poor Planning

I spent many happy years living in the North Pole and helping Father Christmas. I continued to have lots of disasters but somehow we always found a way to clear up my mess. I also started to pick up on sentences that were frequently used in my presence.

"Why would you say that?"

"What were you thinking?"

"Why would you do that?"

"Quick, get a mop!"

"Don't worry, we can always make another one."

Above all I became an expert at making excuses and coming up with heartfelt apologies. But for some reason Father Christmas still loved me and he was often sending me 'out of the way' to help someone or other out.

For example, there was the day when a very distressed looking creature with long ears, big teeth, large feet and a fluffy tail came hopping into Father Christmas' workshop.

"Father Christmas, please can you help me? I'm not going to finish all of my deliveries on time."

"That is such a shock Easter Bunny, you're normally so organised. How have you managed to fall behind schedule?"

"It's all because of the chocolate shortage," said the Easter Bunny with a sigh.

"None of us could have predicted the chocolate drought," said Father Christmas. "So how can I help you? Surely all your eggs are ready now?"

"Of course!" said the Easter Bunny. "But my deliveries should have started 6 hours, 32 minutes and 12 seconds ago and if I don't get some help I'll still be delivering after 6am when some children will be awake! Can I please borrow one of your elves to help drop off these eggs?"

Father Christmas looked very worried. "This is a very crucial time for us. All our elves are very busy trying to produce a new electronic toy which is controlled by the power of the mind."

"Oh please Father Christmas, please. I only have 6 hours, 31 minutes and 17 seconds now!" begged the Easter Bunny, who had got down onto his knees.

"Well, maybe there is someone I can spare.... Adrian!"

I was delighted. He'd obviously chosen his most efficient elf to carry out such an important task.

And after a click of the Easter Bunny's fingers, I was suddenly in an enormous room full of multi-coloured eggs.

Easter Egg Organisation

The Easter Bunny explained to me that these Easter Eggs had to be delivered to every child across the world! The Easter Bunny's job was as hard as Father Christmas', yet the big fella seemed to get a lot more credit than floppy ears. (Please promise me that you will not call the Easter Bunny by that name!)

"Do you have any help?" I asked.

"Well yes, and no," said the Bunny. "I have Easter chicks but they can't be left on their own. I have to stay with them and tell them exactly what to do."

"Hmm." I thought. That sounded rather familiar to me. "So when do you deliver these eggs?"

I immediately regretted asking that question as I could see it was causing the Easter Bunny great pain. His eyes welled up with tears and he had to pause before he could answer.

"They won't give me a definite date, it drives me crazy. All I'm told is that Easter might be in March or it might be in April." The Easter Bunny took a deep breath. "How can I plan like that?"

He then showed me a timetable that stated exactly when each egg would be delivered, how many children would be receiving the eggs, how many eggs were needed, what shape, size and colour the eggs would be and most crucially, the details of any allergies the children had.

"So how can I help?" I asked.

"Well, for one thing, I have to make you a different colour. If anyone sees a bogey coloured elf delivering Easter eggs, it will put them right off their food!"

I was about to explain that my mum thought I was very handsome when I noticed that my arms, legs, hands, feet, body and face were turning pink, and I kind of liked it!

"I also need you to learn more words so we can have a proper conversation," said the

Easter Bunny, who then gave me a dictionary to study and promised to give me English lessons twice a week.

"Can I load these eggs into your basket?" I asked him.

"I am afraid that I can't let anyone interfere with packing or loading as you'd ruin my system. But you can help with my deliveries once I've shown you exactly what to do."

So for the next few hours all I had to do was 'stay out of the way'. And I did exactly that. Well, apart from sitting on an egg and getting chocolate all over my bottom and then spilling a huge container of cream over some Easter chicks who ran all over the workshop and left creamy footprints everywhere.

The Easter Bunny really was amazing. His workshop was split into ten thousand sections. Each section had a million eggs. Each egg was decorated slightly differently and colour coded. And each egg had its own unique reference number.

Easter Egg Deliveries

The Easter Bunny called out a long list of numbers, letters and colours and then clicked his fingers. One second later the Easter Bunny, three chicks, the eggs and me arrived at a large eight-bedroom house. This was a much better way of travelling than Father Christmas used, I thought to myself.

"You need to listen very carefully to these very important instructions."

Oh oh, I thought.

"No problem," I lied.

If I wrote down all of the instructions the Easter Bunny gave me then this would be the longest book ever and nobody would ever want to read it. There would be twenty-five pages explaining how to carry the eggs. Eighty-five pages suggesting appropriate hiding places. Did you know that an oven is a bad place to hide an egg? As is a toilet and a cat litter tray and a dog's bowl! There were also instructions about the chicks and chocolate as well but I was so bored by then that I just signed everything without even reading it.

The one thing I did listen to was the fact that the Easter chicks and I had to hide the eggs in the four downstairs rooms.

I decided that it made more sense if we all went to one room each. What could go wrong?

I gave one of the chicks a red bag labelled: 1467864THF3465C/0601TW01.

Another chick was given the blue bag: 8906547WHL3678A/1208HW02.

The last chick was left with the green bag: 7364537SPR1882S/0207LC03.

I took the pink bag: 1777140AJC1434U/0901SW73.

I studied the house plans and discovered that my room was downstairs and third on the left. It belonged to a girl aged 7 years, 6 months, 12 days, 25 minutes and 17 seconds. I knew I had to watch out for her pink fluffy slippers that would be on the floor by her door and might be a trip hazard.

I had seven eggs to hide. All I had to decide was where best to put the eggs.

In her ears?

Up her nose?

In her mouth?

No!

For some reason none of these places were on my list. Instead I chose the following hiding places:

In a sock.

Stuck inside a lampshade.

Inside a very well painted toy car (which I recognised for some reason).

Underneath a depressed teddy (also familiar).

Stuck on the sharp end of a pencil (not the rubb
end).

In a cup of tea.

Taped under her smelly armpit.

I made those last two places up myself!

I was delighted to have finished so quickly without waking anyone up. I truly was a genius. Now it was time to see how well these chicks had done. I wasn't even slightly worried because they'd been helping the Easter Bunny for years.

Everything was quiet as I walked towards the three rooms where the chicks were. No-one was stirring, so our mission must have been a success.

ere but strangely it had not
eggs. In fact the eggs were still
in the centre of the room and had hundreds of

tiny holes in them. The chick had been pecking
all of the Easter eggs and they were ruined. Now
it was pecking the furniture in the room as well.
Whenever I tried to catch the chick it just flapped
its wings and scuttled away from me. It was far too
fast for me, I was never going to catch it, but if I
didn't do something quickly the whole room was
going to be pecked apart.

I hoped that the chick next door would be able to
help.

Room Two

Disaster again! In the middle of the room sat a huge chick with chocolate smeared all over her. It was on her wings, her face, her legs and her feet. She had blown up to the size of a large football and was now happily munching on a wardrobe. I tried to move her but she was too heavy. I couldn't even roll her out of the room. Surely the third chick could help me?

to be the worst room of all. All of
ı smashed into a million pieces.
ıw flapping about the room
ᵤₑₛₜroying everything. It had pushed
the bedside lamp onto the floor, ripped down the
curtains, torn the duvet, smashed a TV, pooped
in some slippers, and left a terribly smelly mess
on the pillow. There
was a mad look in the
chick's eyes and as
soon as it saw me it
became even more

terrifying as it fluffed
up its feathers, flapped its wings furiously and
raced in my direction. I'm sure you'll agree there's
nothing as scary as a baby chick in full flight.

I turned and ran into the room next door called the kitchen. I didn't like this room when I was a brussel and I still don't like it nowadays! I wasn't sure if I could stand the heat so I turned around to leave. Oh no! There in the doorway were three mad chicks licking their lips. A small part of my brain told me I should've listened to the instructions I was given. There was definitely something written in the forms I signed about not leaving chicks alone and a warning about the dangers of chocolate.

"Ouch!" I screamed. The tiny chick had just pecked me on my little toe.

I wasn't going to wait to let the large chick take a huge chunk out of me, so I bravely chose the following course of action:

Run!

Bang!

My nose slammed straight into yet another table, spilling its contents all over the floor. Hundreds of small round bread things with little black dots fell onto the floor. They all had a symbol on top. Apparently that symbol is called a cross and the bread things are hot cross buns that are baked to remind some people about another hero of theirs.

The chicks started pecking, munching and smashing these obviously delicious buns.

So, first the eggs had been ruined, and now the hot cross buns were being scoffed. I'd managed to ruin Easter.

"Please stop!" I cried.

And the chicks did exactly that, before looking up at me with friendly eyes. They seemed really cute all of a sudden.

"Please could you get out of this house?"

The chicks immediately turned and walked straight out of the front door into the garden where the Easter Bunny was waiting.

"I presume everything went okay?" asked the Easter Bunny.

"Not exactly," I admitted. When I explained what had happened the Easter Bunny was amazed.

"How did you calm the chicks down? Once they've eaten chocolate they become hyper and no-one can control them."

"I just gave them some hot cross buns and asked them nicely to stop!" I replied. "But Easter is still ruined because some of those children don't have any eggs."

"Oh no it isn't," said the Easter Bunny. "I always carry spare eggs. And now you've made my deliveries much easier by showing me how to control those chicks. Thank you Adrian, you have saved Easter!"

There was that feeling again - pride!

So next time you're eating a hot cross bun, please remember that we do this for two reasons - to protect ourselves from vicious Easter chicks and to remember a very special day.

The Time I Nearly Ruined the Tooth Fairy's Life

Too Many Teeth

I continued to live with the Easter Bunny who was true to his word about giving me regular English lessons and so I now had a much larger vocabulary than when I was just a sprout.

I was actually in the middle of one of these lessons when the most incredibly beautiful-looking fairy fluttered through the window and landed beside us.

"Oh Easter Bunny, I really need some help desperately," said the prettiest fairy in the sky. "There's a tooth crisis at Rugby school. Everyone played a game this morning where someone runs with the ball in their hands while everybody else has to chase them and then beat them up."

"That sounds like a ridiculous game," said the Easter Bunny. "Why can't they just kick the ball like civilised people?"

"I agree. It's a ridiculous game but I now have one thousand teeth to pick up from this boarding school tonight and I don't have time to collect all of them. I need someone to help me make the pick-ups!"

"I help can, I help can!" I shouted, but my words did not sound right.

"I'm too scared to help!" exclaimed Easter Bunny. "You know I'm terrified of teeth."

The fairy looked upset and her wide eyes filled with tears as her eyelids started to flutter.

I raised both my hands as high as they would go. I was determined to get their attention. "I for you do anything will!"

But they both looked at me as if I was talking nonsense.

The Easter Bunny scratched his long ears as a plan popped into his furry head. "I might know someone who's silly enough...I mean brave enough to help you. Adrian, meet the Tooth Fairy."

"Yesssss!" I screamed. "I'm your fumber one nan."

Everyone seemed confused by my outburst. But the fairy still came over to introduce herself.

"Hi, I'm the Tooth Fairy."

"I nove that lame," I admitted.

As I looked straight into her gorgeous blue eyes I was wholly captivated. My legs went all wobbly. I could feel my heart beating faster.

"I am very meet to pleased you."

"Why thank you," said the tooth fairy, her face glowing with warmth. "Could you help me pick up some teeth?" she asked.

Had she asked me to eat a slug for lunch I'd have happily done it. I would even have eaten beetles

for pudding with frogspawn sauce, and I would probably have asked for seconds too.

"I would teeth to collect some love." The words coming out of my mouth were definitely not the words my brain was telling it to say. (I still have that problem nowadays too).

"That's great. Hold onto my hand and let's get going." She obviously didn't care that I was acting a little bit strangely.

An Amazing Journey

Hold her hand! I was actually going to hold her hand! Was it too soon to ask her to marry me?

I reached out my hand and suddenly had this terrible feeling that it was a bit sweaty. How could I explain this?

"My wet are hands because I have just toiletted them after washing?"

"I don't care," said the kind fairy. "We have got work to do."

I wiped my hand on my trousers to get rid of the sweat and grabbed onto her hand. Her touch was electric. My body felt like it was turning to jelly. We lifted up into the air and within seconds we were above the clouds. I was flying, but I wasn't slightly interested in that, I was too busy admiring her sparkly wings. I was never going to let go. (Probably just as well as I would have fallen to the ground and landed in a splat!)

The journey was a long one but it was better than flying business class and I also got to learn lots of interesting things about the Tooth Fairy.

1. She makes terrible tea.

2. She loves to watch medical dramas and thinks she could be a doctor.

3. She cries at the end of every sad film. In fact even somebody stepping on an ant sends her into floods of tears.

4. She uses an electric blanket, even in the summer.

5. She's incredibly brave and strong. But I bet I could still beat her in a play fight!

"Are you okay?" asked the lovely fairy.

"I have better been never."

"I need to explain some things about this job, it is very dangerous," said my future wife (I hoped!).

At this time I was no longer taking in anything she was saying. Just the sound of the words coming from that perfectly formed mouth were enough to send me into a trance. As you will discover though, I really should have listened to these words of wisdom, they might have saved me from a number of injuries.

I have written these instructions for you in case the Tooth Fairy ever asks you to help her.

1. Teeth are perfectly safe when they are stuck in your gums.

2. Teeth are also safe for a short time after coming out of your mouth.

3. Teeth that have come out of the gums are harmless as long as they are covered by a pillow.

I agree that so far teeth sound perfectly wonderful. But trust me they are not:

4. Teeth that escape from under the pillow are extremely dangerous.

5. There are smaller, more rounded teeth that will quickly tear you.

6. There are some very large teeth that can crush you.

7. There are pointed, sharp teeth that will cut you.

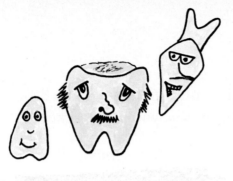

Nowadays I understand that the Tooth Fairy really did have the most dangerous job ever (even more deadly than a teacher). Basically the Tooth Fairy's job is to take the teeth from under pillows and safely put these savage beasts immediately into a fairy pot before transporting them back to a room full of teeth.

However, on my way to my first ever pick up, all I knew was that the Tooth Fairy had the most glorious, long flowing blonde hair. I hadn't really heard anything else apart from the words 'teeth', 'pillow' and 'dangerous'. (But even I knew that pillows were not dangerous so I guessed I had misheard that bit).

"Ok, here's our destination. Are you sure you know what you have to do?"

"Yes. Just take the pillows from under the pot and put them in the fairy tooth."

"Almost!" she laughed. "You visit the rooms downstairs and I'll go upstairs."

"KO," I replied.

"But before you go, I just need to make you a little bit bigger and stronger in case you get attacked."

I didn't listen to the last bit of that sentence because I was too busy admiring my newly formed body. I was much taller now, way over six feet tall. I had muscles everywhere. Even my muscles had muscles. I looked like a Greek God and I still look exactly the same even now (so my mum says!).

"Just use your common sense," said the Tooth Fairy.

Wow! She actually thought I had common sense! This was not something I'd been famous for in the past. I was in love. I started to plan our honeymoon: A huge muddy field with ensuite puddles and maybe then a day trip to the North Pole.

Dormitories

As I walked towards the first door my head was only full of thoughts of the wonderful Tooth Fairy and her perfectly formed wings.

In hindsight I probably shouldn't have let myself be quite so distracted before I carried out this deadly mission!

Dormitory One

I tiptoed into this large room and was amazed to see so many beds in one place. The dormitory was echoing with the sound of snoring and there was a definite smell of sweaty armpits and smelly bottom burps. I tried to be as quiet as I could as I walked towards the first bed, but I still managed to trip over a shoe. Luckily a jumbo jet could have landed in this room without waking the boys up.

My first pillow awaited me. I lifted it up very carefully and peered cautiously underneath.

Zoom!

Out shot a tiny but very fast little tooth. In a flash it sped out of bed, across the floor, through the door and down the hallway.

There was no way I was going to be able to catch it. Would anybody notice that one little tooth was missing? Surely the Tooth Fairy had so many teeth at her house that she wouldn't spot that one was absent. I can't imagine she visits the huge room full of teeth every day to take a register!

"How is everything going?"

"Better be couldn't," I replied.

Time for dormitory two. More caution needed.

Dormitory Two

Yuk! Why do teenage boys smell so bad?
Apparently it's something to do with not using
'anti de-perspirant'? Personally I never use the
stuff. Maybe that's why some people say I smell
'rabbity'!

I decided to crawl along the floor this time,
which meant my head was at a perfect height to
smash into a bedside table (again!) and cause me
maximum pain.

After about 10 minutes of crying I lifted a pillow
and found a
large, slightly
blunt tooth.

It didn't look
dangerous at
all.

I reached
in to pull
it out but
immediately
felt a
crushing
pain.

I was too busy trying to kiss my pancake-like fingers better to notice that this tooth had also managed to escape.

"Did I hear a scream?" said a gentle voice.

"It's okay. I just drew on a stepping pin."

I wasn't having a good night. I'd collected exactly zero out of three teeth so far. I wasn't going to win employee of the month now!

Dormitory Three

This was my last chance to impress and I was determined to leave no stone (pillow) unturned. Crawling along on my belly seemed like the best option this time, which was fine until I crawled over something wet. Yuk!

I reached the pillow and cautiously peered under it.

"Grrrrrrrrr!"

I had no idea that teeth growled. But I did know that I had to grab it and put it immediately into a fairy pot.

"Grrrrrrrrrrrr!"

This tooth looked dangerous. I wished I had gloves on. But still I reached in to grab it.

Big mistake!

The tooth bit me really hard on the end of the finger.

"Ouch!" I screamed.

It bit me again.

"Double ouch!" I screamed.

"Have you been bitten?"

"Fine, I am no." I lied.

This tooth seemed to like the taste of me and it looked ready for seconds, thirds, and fourths.

(This was the one and only time I wished I was a brussel sprout again!)

Showing the courage of a lion, I turned and ran as fast as my huge body builder's legs would carry me, being careful to jump over the warm puddle this time.

Foolishly I looked over my shoulder as I ran out of the dormitory, and of course, I ran into another table!

Naturally on this table was something breakable and naturally this object fell off and broke.

Smash!

The glass container splintered into a million pieces. Its contents went everywhere. The floor was covered in lots of round silver discs. The teeth must have heard the noise because they were all advancing towards me menacingly. I closed my eyes and prepared for the worst.

But no pain came.

So I opened my eyes.

The teeth were right in front of me, standing perfectly still, just staring at the coins.

"Ooh, shiny!" they kept repeating.

My beloved tooth fairy fluttered downstairs after hearing the crashing, the screaming and the sobbing.

"What's happened here?"

"I'm so sorry, I've ruined everything again."
At least I could talk properly now, probably something to do with the fact that I'd received so many blows to my head.

"No you haven't, you've found out something amazing. Teeth get hypnotised by the sight of money. This will make my pick-ups so much easier."

And with that she kissed me on the cheek, or at least I think she did because I fainted just before anything happened.

Next time you put a tooth under your pillow and wake up in the morning to find a coin in its place, please remember why the Tooth Fairy does this!

The End

What Now?

Lots of people ask me if I did eventually marry the Tooth Fairy. Well the answer is no, not yet, but we are engaged now.

I am also asked what do I do for a living now? Well I still help out Father Christmas, the Easter

Bunny and the Tooth Fairy when they need me. Cupid once asked me to help him, but it was decided that giving me a bow and arrow might really be too dangerous!

My main job now is to visit schools and to tell them my amazing story and to try to encourage all of the children to tell me their stories too.

Do you have a story you could tell me?

If you do please write it on **storytellingisfun.com**

Acknowledgements

Lily for being the reason behind everything I do.

Sophie for being my inspiration.

James for being an artistic genius (and his parents for their support).

Thomas and Harry for their wonderful ideas.

Mum and Sylv for giving me my love of books.

My brother Adam for his enthusiasm and for believing in me.

Piers for being a great friend, father figure, godfather and all.

Paula for her passion and technical wisdom.

Lisa for her advice and thoughtful recommendations.

Jeni for her dog walks and company.

Michael and Suzanne for their great friendship.

Elaine, a head teacher, who never lost faith in me.

Father Christmas, the Easter Bunny and the Tooth Fairy for their never-ending patience.

Please visit my website: storytellingisfun.com

where you can:

- Read or write your own stories and send them to me.

- Read other people's ideas.

- Enter competitions.

- Join in some fun games.

- Get some great advice on how to write.

- Watch some storytelling blogs.

- Look at some illustrations.

- Share ideas and ask questions.

storytellingisfun.com

Rediscovering the joy of stories.